Mystery E

# of Dorset

by Chris Moiser

First published in 2007 by:
Inspiring Places Publishing
2 Down Lodge Close
Alderholt
Fordingbridge
Hampshire
SP63JA
ISBN 978-0-9552061-6-0

Other titles by Inspiring Places Publishing:
Fossils and rocks of the Jurassic Coast
Ancient Dorset
Day Tours in the East of Dorset
Smugglers' Dorset
Mysterious Places of Dorset
Dark Age Dorset

Order books and prints at

www.inspiringplaces.co.uk

Contents

*Photographs on pages 10,13,22,28 by Robert Westwood
Others by the author unless stated.*

Introduction

The sightings of exotic big cats in the British Isles have been traditionally associated with Surrey, Devon and Cornwall or Scotland. In the last twenty years or so there have been an increasing number of sightings of these mysterious animals in Dorset. As has happened in the rest of the country these sightings were initially treated with some scepticism, leading to an initial reluctance of witnesses to come forward. However, as the number of witnesses increased and patterns emerged, both in relation to the animals' descriptions and their geographical locations, the stories have started to be believed.

Biologists variously refer to the animals sighted as "exotic", because they are from overseas, "alien" again because they are from overseas, or "beasts", as in the "Beast of Bodmin", because the term is a bit nondescript, but suggests an unknown mammal from a certain area. More specific local names also occur, within Dorset the Beast of Bridport, the Beast of Broadwindsor and the Beast of Westham are all local names that have been commonly used.

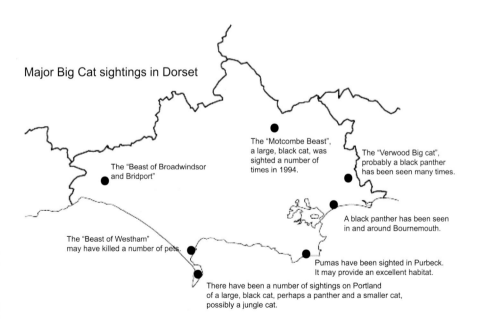

Major Big Cat sightings in Dorset

The "Beast of Broadwindsor and Bridport"

The "Motcombe Beast", a large, black cat, was sighted a number of times in 1994.

The "Verwood Big cat", probably a black panther has been seen many times.

A black panther has been seen in and around Bournemouth.

The "Beast of Westham" may have killed a number of pets.

Pumas have been sighted in Purbeck. It may provide an excellent habitat.

There have been a number of sightings on Portland of a large, black cat, perhaps a panther and a smaller cat, possibly a jungle cat.

The Cats

Zoologists divide the thirty-eight or so species of the cat family into two main groups, the five big cats, who can all roar, and the thirty-three or so smaller cats, who can purr, but not roar. Simply the big cats are the lion, tiger, leopard, jaguar and snow leopard. The smaller cats are the remaining species. In this book the term big cat will be used for anything bigger than the ordinary domestic cat.

The cats sighted in the Dorset area usually come clearly within one of three descriptions:

a). A 'large brown cat with a short tail or no tail'
This may have patterns within its coat and the male may appear to have a mane – typically this would be a lynx, although there is a smaller animal with the same body pattern from North America called the bobcat or Bay lynx. The European lynx is known to have lived in the British Isles until at least the sixth century and possibly until more recently.

b). A 'large brown cat with a long tail'
From the description and size this is fairly likely to be a puma. The puma is the largest of the "small" cats in zoological terms. It is also a very adaptable cat existing in a variety of habitats in the Americas from where it originally came. Although the media often refer to black pumas they do not occur in captivity and until recently were

Above: A puma © Paul Crowther, Newquay Zoo
Below left: A European lynx

thought only to have been recorded once or twice in the historical past
in the wild. It seems likely now that a population of black or very dark
brown pumas may occur in parts of Colorado. A dark brown puma
could appear black, if seen on a dark night, when wet. The puma still
occurs over very large areas of the Americas. This cat is very secretive
and because it will adapt to the prey that is available, it is regularly
found in States where it was previously thought to be extinct. It has
never lived naturally in Europe although one survived in the wild for
some time in Scotland before being captured.

c). A 'large black cat with a long tail'
Generally these are referred to as black panthers. The word panther
can get confusing because in the UK it generally refers to a (black)
leopard, whilst in the USA it can refer to a puma (e.g. the Florida
panther is the local subspecies of puma in Florida). The black leopard
is just a genetic variant of the ordinary leopard and may cross-breed
freely with "spotted leopards". However, if a black leopard mates with
a black leopard any resulting cubs will always be black. The coat,
although black, will, if looked at in the right light, be seen to have spots
of different shades within the black. The leopard is the smallest of the

5

big cats and probably has the biggest range of any wild cat; being present throughout sub-Saharan Africa and much of Asia. It was formerly present in Europe, including Great Britain, and probably became extinct in the British mainland about 12,000 years ago.

The other big cat that sometimes comes in the black coat colour is the jaguar. Although scarce in the wild, the black jaguar occurs commonly enough to have been exhibited in a few British zoos. Some of the smaller species of cat may also occasionally occur with a black coloured coat (or in the melanistic form). Melanistic smaller cats, if they occurred here in the wild, would probably, from a distance, be mistaken for domestic cats. This has occurred with melanistic bobcats in Florida.

Other species of exotic cat that have been found dead in the United Kingdom, rather than just being seen, include leopard cats and jungle cats. These have been imported in some numbers and are currently kept by some private individuals for cross-breeding with domestic cats to create the "Bengal" and "Chausie" variety of cat respectively. In fact the individuals of these species that have been found wild here have either been shot or found as road kill, typically without any reports of them being seen in the area first.

Many of these animals were found before it became fashionable to keep them for cross-breeding with domestic cats. These two cross-bred cat species are often slightly bigger than the ordinary domestic cat and, because of their appearance, may be mistaken for a more exotic cat species. Certainly a Bengal cat in the north of Plymouth has been mistaken, on separate occasions, for both an ocelot and a serval!

One other possibility exists and that is that these animals seen living wild in Dorset and other counties are hybrids of some sort. A hybrid is a cross between two species. Such an animal will typically show characteristics of both parent species. Hybrids tend to occur in captivity rather than in the wild and are usually sterile.

Against the normal rules however, a hybrid has occurred in the wild in the United Kingdom, and that is a cat called the Kellas cat, which is found in some parts of Scotland and appears to be some strange sort of cross between the European (Scottish) wild cat and the domestic cat. There is, in the future, also the possibility that the European wild cat in Scotland may hybridise with the Bengal or Chaussie mentioned previously. Whether or not this will be successful, and what the kittens will be like, remains to be seen.

With the exception of the lion, all the cat species are normally solitary animals except when they come together to breed, or where a mother is living with kittens. When studied where they naturally occur the larger species of cats typically have a territory of something like seven to twenty square miles depending partly on the availability of food. Males may have a bigger territory which overlaps the territories of several females. The animal's territory is usually marked with dung and urine sprays. As cats have a sense of smell that is millions of times better than the human one, this is an effective way of marking boundaries.

Territories may also be partly determined by the existence of the next animal's territory, so if in the UK we have a small number of, say, black leopards, it is likely that they are not all occupying neighbouring territories. This would mean that they could wander for long distances without necessarily coming into contact with another animal's territory. In other words their territories may be larger than those normally quoted in the standard text books.

Where the animal does have an established territory it will frequently move around that territory in a set pattern, often, in the case of a leopard, having a "circuit time" of something like twenty-eight to thirty-five days. In the event of being disturbed, it may break that circuit pattern and avoid the place where it was disturbed for several months.

Right: A black panther. The "Beast of Broadwindsor and Bridport" may be an animal such as this.

How did they get here?

A question commonly asked about these animals is how they came to be in the United Kingdom? The answer is far from clear and frankly we do not know. There are a number of possible explanations which vary in how believable they are. Some are supported for reasons that do not really stand up to scientific examination.

Prehistoric survivors – The idea being that they were always here. This is very unlikely. The puma was never here and the leopard and lynx have been extinct for so long a period that it seems highly unlikely, in a country with a human population density such as that in Britain, that a large predator would go un-noticed. The situation with the European wild cat is a little more uncertain because it is not really known when they became extinct in southern England. One of the major researchers in this area, Derek Yalden, believes that the European wild cat was extinct in the whole of southern England by the 1800s (Yalden 1999, 177). Various natural history societies have suggested other dates, but it is possible that the animals hung on longer. It is also possible that they hybridised with feral domestic cats to produce something like the Kellas cat (the hybrid cat found in some parts of Scotland).

Zooform phenomena – This is the "ghosty idea", the idea that these animals are something like ghosts of exotic cats that died here at some time in the past, possibly when present in circuses or menageries. Such "spirits" could not settle because they are so far from home. The idea is not capable of scientific test, and unless there is something specific about cats making them more likely to become a "ghost" than other species, there should, if the idea had any credence, be a range of other ghostlike species sighted, including elephants, bears, rhinos and assorted hoofstock.

 The other idea to explain a non-physical entity is that they are a primal memory from our evolutionary past when, as an early ape walking upright, we would have been regularly preyed upon by large cats. The ability to recognise any glimpse of a large predator such as a big cat may have had survival value. Such an explanation might explain a momentary glimpse by a single witness, but it doesn't explain the situation where several witnesses see the animal at once, photographs are taken or it is seen hunting prey.

Above: A leopard cat

Captive releases, intentional or accidental – There are a number of ways in which this could have happened. The classic explanation loved by the media is that the animals were released when the Dangerous Wild Animals Act 1976 came into force. It appears to explain the phenomena in one or two sentences. Owners of the exotic animals could not afford a licence and insurance when the Act came into force. As there was no government help for them, they were faced with having to get rid of the animal(s) in their possession, at their own expense. The zoos of the day were unable to accept the numbers offered and rather than have them euthanased (a polite term for humanely killed), they released them in suitably remote areas.

There is actually little evidence of this having happened; despite claims made in 2000 by a "Retired Lion Tamer" from the West Midlands. It would certainly not explain the sightings of animals made in the 1960s in Hampshire, Surrey, Devon and Cornwall. There is also the intriguing question as to why, in the periods immediately after the release, a number of sightings of semi-tame wild cats of diverse species were not seen. In fact during the four year period immediately after the Act came into force hardly any cat sightings are reported anywhere in the United Kingdom. There is a report though

Above: Rich, arable farmland such as this on Cranborne Chase could easily provide a living for a big cat.

of a man from Blackley, Manchester being prosecuted for being in possession of a puma within 3 days of the Act coming into force. This animal had escaped from the garden shed where it was being kept. Strangely, it was not an offence to release exotic animals into the British countryside until 1981, five years after the Dangerous Wild Animals Act came into force.

What is more likely to have happened is that animals in private ownership may have escaped from sub-standard accommodation at almost anytime. Another thought is also that the travelling menageries of the eighteenth and nineteenth century may have had unreported escapes of animals, or even released animals that they could no longer afford to feed. The wear and tear on "beast wagons" imposed by the roads of the period would make regular escapes more likely. Most of the reported escapes do, however, seem to include details of a rapid recapture, or shooting of the animal. The menageries frequently passed through Dorset on their way to Devon and Cornwall. A report of one visiting Exeter in 1806 referred to the collection being visited, whilst in Weymouth, "by his Grace the Duke of Cumberland, Lord Derby, Lord Poulet and family and all the rest of the nobility and gentry". This collection was housed in five caravans and included a "Bengal tiger, a lion and lioness, panthers, leopards, a hyena, a lynx, a kangaroo and an ostrich".

Private collections of animals in history may also have been responsible for escapes, although whether these were short term or

10

had a longer term effect is unclear. Although there are no records of large historic private collections in Dorset, it is known that, just across the border in Wiltshire, there was a private collection of exotic animals at Longleat that well preceded the first of the modern zoos and safari parks. Indeed, records reveal that in the winter of 1733/34, Robert, a carpenter, was paid eight shillings and four pence for five days work in making a cage for the leopard.

Another possibility is the idea of a deliberate release, not to dispose of animals but to attempt a reintroduction; almost a "mad scientist scenario". This idea was suggested in February 2002 when the "Rural Guerillas", part of the Wild Beast Trust, claimed that they had released lynx into selected woods in Scotland. They came up with a further claim in September 2006 when the possibility of an illegal (i.e. unlicensed) release of wolves was also suggested for the north of England. Their objective is to re-establish extinct British species.

The other reason for a deliberate release is with a view to hunting the animals. West Yorkshire police seized two unlicensed lynx from an outside shed behind a house in Rastrick in 2000. The owner said they were going to be released for hunting. Rumours of lynx being released for hunting were also circulating at the game fair in Shepton Mallet, across the border in Somerset, in 2002.

Why Dorset?

Dorset represents one of the best possible habitats for introduced and re-introduced species of cat, and other types of animal, in southern England. The county has had a long agricultural history and has a relatively low human population density compared with the rest of southern England. Additionally there are a range of habitats varying from the Jurassic Coast to heathlands and woodlands. The Forestry Commission maintain several large areas of woodland. Two of these, Wareham and Ringwood Forests, have extensive visitor access, but still get their regular share of exotic cat sightings. These woodlands support large deer populations which are a major potential food source and, according to local naturalist Jonathan McGowan, these deer populations are now starting to show signs of predation by big cats. Also the farmed land supports a large rabbit population which is another major food source.

Possible early cats:

Robin Young's manuscript "Reminiscences of Sturminster Newton" which was published in 1907 carries a reference of a wild and monstrous cat with eyes as big as tea saucers. This animal is said to have haunted the top of Newton Hill next to the castle ruins at Sturminster Newton. Local people would apparently avoid the area in case they saw this animal. A similar story is also told at Friar Waddon near Portesham, where the large black cat had penetrating eyes and a luminous tail! There is also a legend of a "Shillingstone Castle Cat". The Sturminster Newton area continues to be associated with big cat sightings to the present day and there were also reports of sheep killings in the area in 1999, when the expression "The Beast of Blackmore Vale" was coined.

More recent sightings

The Forestry Commission have extensive land in Hampshire and in Dorset. In response to a recent request they revealed a list of over thirty sightings within this area. Their earliest record is of a "black panther" seen at Shatterford, "bounding across heathland" in 1980. Shatterford is, of course, in Hampshire but the Hampshire - Dorset border does present an ideal habitat with the edges of the New Forest and Ringwood Forest supplying food and cover. Sightings in this area will be considered in the "Cats to the East of the County" section.

The Beast of Broadwindsor and Bridport

Broadwindsor is a village in west Dorset that started to have regular sightings of a big black cat in September 1994. The first reported sighting was described in the Dorset Evening Echo of the eighth of September. Vincent Gavigan of Broadwindsor Stores was delivering papers early in the morning when he saw a large animal blocking the road near Lower Park. He drove within about thirty-five yards of it and stopped to get out and look, but the animal looked at him and then jumped across the hedge into the fields and disappeared. This relieved Mr. Gavigan somewhat as he said that it was the size of an Alsatian dog, but more portly. Its head was like a puma, its eyes were

Above: Heathland such as this on the Isle of Purbeck near Studland may provide a good habitat for big cats. Traditionally there have been relatively frequent sightings on the heathland and Forestry Commission land in east Dorset and in the New Forest, over the border in Hampshire.

green. He was, apparently, startled to learn that his description of the animal exactly matched that of the Beast of Bodmin that was in the news at this time.

A week later the same newspaper reported another sighting, this time by local estate agent Frank Smith, who saw it on a bright morning near Bucks Head, just south of Lewesdon Hill. His description of the animal matched the earlier one and he described the movement of the animal as "loping like a cat". Several of the villagers have since told Mr. Smith that they too had sighted the animal.

A few months later and a few miles further south, at Salway Ash, a large cat was seen again and the police and RSPCA are now taking the reports much more seriously. Chief Inspector David Steel, RSPCA is advising people not to approach the animal, if seen, and to report sightings immediately to them, or to the police at Bridport.

Three months later, in May (1995) another big cat is seen a little further south at Symondsbury. The witness this time was Mrs Beverley Attinger, a woman who had previously been totally sceptical of the existence of these animals. She changed her mind however, when she watched a pale-beige coloured animal for two or three minutes from her kitchen window. She called her husband who also saw the animal. She was convinced that it was a big cat and not a dog, having watched a lot of dogs in the same field. She also reported that

13

the cows in the field had moved away from the animal, when they would normally move towards a dog. This cat was not black and therefore not the same one that had been seen previously.

Sightings in the area continued over the next few years. In March 1997 antiques dealer Cliff Gibbs saw the animal at Broadwindsor again and the following month Stuart Dunn saw a large panther-like creature slinking under a gate near West Milton. In May 1997 Richard Austin, who took pictures for the Bridport and Lyme Regis News, saw a big black cat whilst out photographing wildlife in the snow at Raymond's Hill. To his embarrassment he tried to take a couple of pictures in the few seconds during which he saw the animal, but they were all unusable. He described the animal as "absolutely jet black", so black that when it turned towards him he couldn't make out its features.

After a few months with no reports there was another sighting of the black beast, this time on the outskirts of Beaminster. Local tree surgeon Simon Beadles saw the animal as he stood with friends in St. Mary's churchyard. As they looked over the River Brit they saw the large black cat "bound" into view on the other side of the river.

In 1998 after a quiet start to the year there was suddenly a rash of sightings in the Symondsbury, Bridport and Burton Bradstock areas in August. Rather hopefully Burton resident Ernest Foster, on

Territorial Range

With each species of cat the individual's home range is determined by the area which it needs to supply adequate food and a mate. The shape of the territory may of course be partly determined by geographical features such as rivers, cliffs and the coast. The published ranges of each of the main species tend to have been measured in countries where they occur naturally and in which the range is partly determined by the pressure from similar animals in neighbouring ranges that want to keep competitors (for food and possible mates) out of their territory. Typically a puma in the States may have a territory as big as 45,000 hectares (180 square miles). Leopards will have a territory of anything in excess of 2,800 hectares (7 square miles), depending upon the prey available, and for the same reasons, a lynx will occupy anything from 1,000 hectares (3.9 square miles) upwards. Each of these animals may travel 40 kilometres (25 miles) in a night. Where the population of any of these cats is small, as in the UK, the range may be greater than normally quoted because there are no neighbouring animals struggling to keep their range exclusive. Similarly lone animals may wander long distances looking for a mate.

seeing the animal as he walked his Labrador towards the beach one evening, instructed the dog to "go get it!". Not surprisingly the dog declined, and the cat just looked and then "shot away".

More alarmingly a month later Joe Tait, a local postman, whilst walking on the western edge of Bridport, saw a large black cat "ripping" into the body of a freshly killed sheep. Mr. Tait's two dogs chased the animal, which easily outran them and disappeared into a spinney at the back of Ryeberry Hill. Mr. Tait had his twelve bore shotgun with him and said that he would have shot the animal had he been a bit closer. The farmer, Alex Gibson, told the Dorset Evening Echo that he had already lost five or six sheep to a mystery predator over the previous few weeks.

In the intervening years a similarly described black cat has been seen on numerous occasions in the Bridport, Beaminster areas and occasionally as far west as Lyme Regis. In early 2004 the Bridport and Lyme Regis News reported that a black animal "much too big to be a domestic cat" had been seen crossing a farmyard. It jumped a hedge and continued down the farm drive towards the A3066. The witness was convinced that it was not a dog.

One noteworthy report was made by Beaminster shepherd Steve Evans, in March 2004. Two days after finding one of his larger sheep dead, and with a lot of meat missing from the body, he sighted what he thought to be a mother with cubs. He was out riding his quad bike along a track which looked down into a steep valley when he noticed, about 200 yards away, what he first thought was a black Labrador dog. Shortly afterwards a second one appeared and they circled a bramble patch. Much to his surprise a large black animal then emerged from the brambles. He described this animal as being the height of an Alsatian, but longer. All the animals had distinctive long, swooping tails that curved up at the end. All were jet black and shiny without any visible patterns within the coat, but in view of the distance he couldn't be sure that there weren't any markings within the coat. After observing them for 15 minutes or so he coasted down to where

15

Left: A puma © Pual Crowther, Newquay Zoo. Pumas are very adaptable creatures and will eat whatever prey is available.

they were without starting his engine. The animals disappeared, leaving behind a pungent odour of a sort that he hadn't smelt before.

Steve had seen another black panther type animal in 2002 during a shoot on neighbouring property. Whilst the shoot was in progress the animal made its way down a hill and into deep cover. Whilst not certain about what he had seen, the sighting was confirmed by several of the people on the shoot.

In June 2006 the Beast of Bridport was allegedly finally photographed by the appropriately named Joy Adamson outside St Swithun's Church in Bridport. She saw what she first thought was a Labrador coming out of the church gates. When it got closer she realised that it was in fact a big cat and took a picture of it with her telephone camera. The picture published on the seventh of June edition of the Bridport Radio shows a slightly artificial looking puma apparently crossing a pedestrian crossing with some out of focus stone pillars to the immediate right of the animal. Discussion on some of the big cat websites later that month suggested that the picture was not genuine.

Later in the same month there was another strange twist to the Beast of Bridport tale when another sighting was reported from the Beaminster area. This time the newspaper reported it as a "tiger-like cat". Ken and Vera Caldwell saw the animal twice within a few days and were hoping to get a picture if it re-appeared. The animal was seen from a distance of about thirty metres by Mr. Caldwell who first of all thought that it was a fox and then saw that it appeared to be striped. Whilst he was watching the animal through binoculars it turned and looked straight at him. His view of the face was that it was wide and flat with short ears, and to Mr. Caldwell's mind, exactly like a tiger. A few days later he and his wife observed the animal again. Both sightings were early in the morning and in good light.

Although not canvassed at the time, because of the size and flat face, the animal that they were describing could have been a red panda. Although native to certain areas in the Far East, red pandas are maintained in several zoological collections and do sometimes, usually as a result of their climbing abilities, escape. One that escaped in France was on the run for three months without suffering any weight loss or other mishaps.

Right: A puma cub - notice the spotted pattern on the coat.

Left: Was a red panda seen near Beaminster in 2006?

Portland, Weymouth and Dorchester

This whole area has had a number of sightings which, although intermittent, do start to form a pattern. In 1988 the Westham area of Weymouth saw a number of children's pets killed. At the time it was suggested that a large feral cat was to blame but the animal was not caught. It was described as being black by those who saw it. In Summer 1989 Hilda Sweeney reported in the Evening Echo that the animal was now being seen regularly amongst Portland's weares. This time it was described as being "a dark, tabby feral cat about the size of a spaniel". Despite the disparity in colour one island resident, Jack Noble, was positive that the "Beast of Westham" and the "Island Moggie" were the same animal. He claimed to have seen this animal chasing a young fox, which itself was chasing a smaller "furry creature".

A later sighting on Portland was reported in September 1995 when Ken Lewington saw what he thought was a "cougar" (an American name for a puma) when walking his dog at the old coal yard, Victoria Place, Easton. He described a long black/grey animal with a shoulder height of about eighteen inches, "moving in a feline fashion with its large tail swishing". His bull terrier dog apparently chased it, and wouldn't come back on demand. This was said to be unusual for the dog.

Two months later a black cat was seen in the deserted early morning streets of Weymouth by Portland van driver Chris Allen. The animal was described as being a big black cat-like creature that was crossing the road to enter the Radipole Nature Reserve. He was of the opinion that, because of its size, it could not be a domestic cat.

February 1996 saw a report of the smaller cat on Portland again. This time a visiting teacher from Wakefield who was staying with friends on the island for half term, Jack Dews, saw what they described as "an animal similar in appearance to a lynx" sunning itself on a cliff face alongside the Grove Road allotments. His description was of an animal about two feet long with a flat face, smooth furred and being a dark grey, striped colour. The description in fact is more like a jungle cat than a lynx.

In 1998 the Black Beast is back in the Westham area of Weymouth. This time it was sighted in late October by a couple travelling home by taxi at 2.00 am. The animal was huge, black and cat-like according to witness Helen Jensen who said that it was "definitely too big to be a domestic cat and it looked more like a panther to me". The animal was seen close to the Swannery for a few seconds before it disappeared into the bushes there.

Two years later in November 2000 we have a black cat reported again, this time in the Church Ope Cove area of Portland. This time a worried member of the public had called the police when a local resident saw a black cat "about the size of an Alsatian" near the cliff. The police attended the area but found nothing. The report of this sighting prompted a couple from Plush, a village about five miles to the north of Dorchester, to report the sighting of a very similar animal that they had made four weeks or so previously. The sighting from Plush was particularly interesting because Mrs. Perks had seen the Labrador-sized black cat rush past her kitchen window. When she reported it to her husband he did not believe her, but a few days later he came face to face with the same animal when he was working near his barn.

As ever with these matters things went quiet for a few months and then in August 2001 a big black cat was sighted at Crossways, to the east of Dorchester. The sighting was associated with the killing of a number of chickens and ducks in a back garden in the same village. There was then another period of quiet when there were no reports made to the newspapers.

This silence was broken with a report of a sighting during the last week of November 2002. This time a large black cat was seen running at high speed across fields behind Dorchester Football Club's grounds at Weymouth Avenue. The witness, rather unconvincingly, said that the animal was as big as a horse and appeared to be chasing something. Despite the rapid attendance of a police car, nothing further was seen. Several local dog walkers who used the area regularly were approached by the Western Gazette reporter and expressed concern for the safety of their dogs.

In 2005, on about the 26th of April, William Willoughby spotted a lynx close to a playground in Westham, Weymouth. He actually saw it from his living room window when he came downstairs, at about 3.00am, for a cigarette. He was sure that it was a lynx and stated that it was three times the size of a domestic cat. It remained close to his window for four or five minutes, snarling at him on a couple of occasions, before jumping the garden wall and disappearing. According to the police report he was in the garden, but according to the Echo report he was indoors. His step-daughter had apparently seen a similar animal some weeks previously in a local alleyway. This sighting wasn't reported in the Echo on the fourth of May but within four days there was another report of a lynx being seen in the same area by another resident. The police also received a report of two domestic cats having disappeared in this area.

A third report was published by the Echo later in the month when Pat Marsh, a schoolteacher, saw what she thought was a lynx at about 9.15 pm in the school grounds of St. Andrew's, at Preston, just north of Weymouth. Another sighting then occurred on the 28th of May, this one went directly to the police and didn't get to the Dorset Echo. A lady out walking her dog saw a lynx at Upwey, to the north-east of Preston.

Interestingly, when commenting on a big cat sighting in the Bournemouth area in August 2005, a Dorset Police wildlife officer, PC John Snellin, said that there were "fairly regular reports" of lynx in the Weymouth area.

Obviously, because of the nature of the land, any animal that gets onto the Portland isthmus is effectively trapped there with a very restricted chance of finding its way off the "island". The size of Portland is such that it could only support one or two medium-sized cats at most and any population there must be regarded as temporary.

On a slightly different theme, Dorset police did have another strange animal report from Portland in January 2006 when they received a telephone call from a member of the public who saw a large "monkey type animal" at lunchtime on the beach at Underhill. There were no further reports of this animal.

What might these cats eat?

One of the remarkable things about all the cat family is the way that they will change their prey according to what is available. Lynx in some parts of their range eat predominantly hares and rodents. In another part of their range they eat mainly reindeer. The puma will eat anything from grasshoppers to bison. Leopards too have a great variety in their diet, having being recorded eating prey from grasshoppers to large antelope at 90kg. In the Serengeti (Tanzania), where leopard have been well studied, gazelle form their main dietary item. With each of the three main species of cat said to be present in Dorset, rabbits and deer would be the main food with possibly some game birds and the odd lamb. Because of the number of deer and rabbits taken these cats would almost certainly be more of an asset to agriculture and forestry than a nuisance. Realistically, 10 - 30 rabbits could be taken each week by any one of these cats.

Wareham and the Isle of Purbeck

This area is of particular interest and yet raises a number of questions. As a habitat it could be one or more individual territories that are largely defined and contained by the rivers and the sea, or it could be part of a larger territory used by either an animal coming in from east Dorset (e.g. the cat seen in Bournemouth and Verwood), or an animal coming in from the Weymouth, Portland, Dorchester area to the west. This latter route seems possible as there have been several sightings of a large black cat in the Crossways and Warmwell area in July 2001, in January 2004 and again in February 2006.

The River Frome is also a good partial barrier that would raise problems for an animal seeking to move regularly from Wareham Forest south into the Isle of Purbeck and for this reason it may form a limit to the ranges of a number of animals.

Although there is a report of a fisherman seeing a large black cat on the cliffs at Lulworth Cove in the 1960s, reports from the Isle of Purbeck are, in the main, fairly recent ones.

On the 10 th of April 2004 three friends were walking on Hartland Moor when they believe that they saw two pumas fall out of a tree. Chris Austen and his wife Sandy were out for a walk with their friend Mrs Hayes when they heard a screech, "an eerie noise, not

Above: The heathland of the New Forest, although popular with humans and dogs; there is plenty of food for wild big cats.

something that you get from a domestic pet", just before the animals fell out of the tree about 40 yards distant from them. This was reported in the Daily Echo of the 15th of April, but according to the Dorset police log actually took place on the tenth.

On the 19th of November 2005 the police log reveals that a puma was sighted in a back garden in "Wareham North" the night before. Various other reports of sightings in the Wareham area in the two years or so before this are given on the Dorset Big Cat register website by witnesses who have responded directly to that website.

At his talk at the Big Cat Conference at Market Trussell in 2006, Jonathan McGowan discussed this area and the sightings that had occurred there. He suggested that the caves in the cliffs in this area might periodically be used as dens by the cats. In view of the amount of time that Jonathan has spent doing fieldwork in this area this observation should be taken seriously.

Cats to the East of the County, or the Verwood Big Cat and the Pennington Panther

The east of Dorset, probably because of the nature of the land and the proximity to the New Forest, has always been a hot spot for big cat sightings. In considering these sightings it is possibly best to consider a strip running from Poole Bay, north to Cranborne. Sightings in this area also need to be considered in conjunction with sightings in Hampshire and the New Forest.

22

A Freedom of Information Act request to the Forestry Commission revealed that they had had reports of a puma drinking from the river near Longham Bridge in the 1980s, but no further details were available from them. In fact this sighting appears to be the one made by Jonathan McGowan, who had also seen a puma stalking near a badger set that he was observing three years previously near Blandford.

The Forestry Commission records then reveal multiple sightings of a black panther in the New Forest during the mid 1990s. Most of these seem to come either directly from the Forest Keeper or via the Forest Keeper, who was presumably the first person to speak to the witness concerned. These reports appear to inter-relate quite nicely with reports starting to appear in the Bournemouth Evening Echo. In particular these refer to the Brockenhurst (Hampshire) Big Cat (November 1993), the Verwood Big Cat (December 1993), the Pennington Panther (June 1994), the Ferndown Jaguar (July 1994), and the Verwood Big Cat (again – September 1994). As well as sightings of this animal there was an attack on two Icelandic horses called Arvakur and Feykir in the Verwood area in September 1994.

Both horses suffered gashes to their flanks and Feykir also had a large bite mark on his throat. The vet who treated both horses confirmed that it was an attack by a large carnivore. Reports in this area of Dorset are then sparse for a few years, but the Forestry Commission reports for the New Forest, particularly the Holly Hatch Inclosure area then start to recur during 1996 and 1997.

A sheep was mauled to death at Edmondsham, to the west of Ringwood Forest, in June 1999. Certain aspects of the case suggested that this was not done by a dog. The Forestry Commission also recorded sightings of a black panther at both Stephens Lane, Verwood and the Ringwood Forest during this month. Two months later the Forestry Commission had yet another report of a black panther, this time at Holt Wood, Ferndown Forest. In their round up of the big cat sightings of the year the magazine Fortean Times was keen to point out that there had been six big cat sightings in a seven mile radius.

In June 2002 the black panther appears again in Ringwood Forest. This time a report of it descending a tree is passed to a Forest Keeper and enters into the Forestry Commission records.

August 2002 had postal worker Bernard Seale driving home at 3.15 am when he saw a large cat cross the road in front of his car on Waterloo Road near Canford Heath. This animal was described as being brown with a tail with a white tip. It also was described as having massive paws and moving in a cat-like manner.

In January 2003, although not in Dorset, there was a report to Hampshire police of a panther seen on the A31 going towards Ringwood, between Picket Hill and Ringwood. This of course is only a few miles from Ringwood Forest and the Verwood area.

As ever when there has been a gap of a few years there is often a sudden flurry of reports and that happened in the Bournemouth area in mid-2005. A report to the police on the 20th of August by Kevin Hammersley, a Devizes man on holiday in Bournemouth, stated that he was walking, with a friend, along Exeter Road in Westcliff at 4:30 am when he was confronted by what he was sure was a puma. Later the same day, at about 8.00pm, a woman who worked in the control room at Dorset Police, was walking her dog on Canford Heath, Poole when she heard a loud roar from behind some bushes. She, her mother, who was also present, and the dog were frightened and so ran. As they ran there was a second roar. Neither the informant nor her mother actually saw anything.

A few days earlier a frightened security man alerted police when he spotted a large black cat while on patrol at the Hurn industrial estate, near the airport. According to the BBC report he

Left: A European lynx. Such cats have been sighted a number of times in the Weymouth area.

was so frightened that he armed himself with a large piece of wood in case of an attack. In a report in the Dorset Echo, PC John Snellin, the local police wildlife officer, stated that they had also had a report three weeks previously of a black cat spooking a horse in a field north of Wimborne, and "fairly regular" sightings of European lynx in the Weymouth area. Whilst pointing out that 99 times out of 100 these cats would run away, the officer did advise the public not to approach them and to dial 999 if they saw one. He also indicated that there were about 30 reports a year of such sightings in Dorset and that the police had a contingency plan if one was to appear.

What PC Snellin didn't mention was another report that had come into the police just over two months earlier, in mid June 2005. This report came from a farmer who lived to the north of Wimborne, between Horton and Holt. On the night before the report was made, the farmer's daughter had seen a "large black animal" attempting to get at his lambs. This farmer had already lost three lambs in the previous few days. What made this attack different to the ordinary dog attack on sheep was that the lambs had been taken from the field by being dragged through the fence.

A couple of days after PC Snellin's statement the Echo reported another possible sheep attack in the area. A ram and three ewes were attacked, but not killed, at White Sheet Hill, Uddens, near Wimborne. Although the attacking animal was not seen, the owners had assumed that it was not a fox because foxes do not generally attack rams. The initial conclusion was that it was dogs, but no dogs had been seen. When Dorset police were approached again, PC Snellin said that there had been three or four sightings of a black cat in the White Sheet Plantation area "in the last month or so". He was also keen to mention that the sightings were from "good level-headed people."

The newspaper reports in turn prompted local resident Carol Lewis to contact the paper and report her sighting of a dark brown cat on the beach at Alum Chine two years previously.

Towards the end of October 2005 Nicholas Rogers, aged 10, had a nasty surprise when running home in Broadstone just north of Poole. As he was passing along Cheam Road he saw a large black animal walking towards him. As he slowed down he got within eight feet of the animal and found that it was about the size of a Labrador with a large strange-shaped head and big yellow eyes. The animal apparently then turned and disappeared into some bushes.

The following week the Dorset police received a report of a black panther being seen in the early hours of the morning in the Bearwood area of Bournemouth. The witness had a good idea of the height of the animal because it walked past a camper van and was higher than the wheels. Broadstone and Bearwood are of course very close to each other with Canford Heath in between.

About two weeks after this a lynx was sighted near Wimborne. The witness reported the sighting to the Big Cats in Britain Research Group, but unfortunately not until the following January. The report seemed genuine though because the witness had seen the animal once, and commented to their partner who was sceptical. The witness and the partner then saw the animal together, in virtually the same place on New Year's Eve 2005 and agreed on the identification of the animal.

Another panther sighting, just across the border in Hampshire, occurred in late April 2006 when Poole student James Barnes was returning, by coach, from London. He spotted an animal across the dual carriageway on the A31 between Stoney Cross and Picket Post at about 7.45 pm. He described the animal as being black with a small head and a long tail. It was apparently close to some ponies, so he had a size reference and was able to say that it was far too big to be a domestic cat.

A quite different type of animal was reported by police officers on an anti-poaching patrol at Edmondsham in October 2003. Jon Kuspert and Richard Lill had an animal jump out in front of them which they followed for some distance. What they saw had a long tail, was grey in colour with coloured markings and a black stripe down its back. The animal was described as being far too big to be a domestic cat and after both officers returned from duty they went straight to the internet. Examination of pictures there led them to believe that what they had seen was a European wild cat. In a major understatement the Dorset Echo reported that this species is found throughout Europe "... including parts of Scotland but is rarely found this far south". In fact the species is generally said to have been extinct in the south of England by the 1800s as previously stated.

Two possibilities exist if the animal was a European wild cat: there was either a small population of them that survived, in say the New Forest, undiscovered for almost 200 years, or there

Left: A jungle cat © Rick Green

had been an illegal (i.e. unlicensed) re-introduction of the animals. The alternative is that the animal was not a European wild cat and was possibly a Bengal or Chausie cat, one of the new hybrid breeds which are often bigger than either parent species. The description could be that of a Bengal, and in 2003 there were fewer pictures of these animals on the internet. Those that were available were unlikely to be found unless one went specifically looking for them, i.e. already knew of the existence of the breed.

The idea of a surviving population of European wild cats may not be totally ridiculous because from a distance these animals might be mistaken for tabby cats, and Dorset is the county where a population of polecats (not in fact cats, but ferret-like animals) were found many years after they were supposed to have died out. There is also a suggestion that the beech marten, a species not previously thought to exist in Britain, may not only have lived in the county, but have survived until recent times in Dorset.

The Motcombe Beast

Motcombe is a village just to the north of Shaftesbury. During August of 1994 there were a number of sightings of a big black cat as well as the discovery of footprints and reports of loud animal noises. In fact this area subsequently had very few reports of big cats until February 2006 when a resident reported to Dorset police that he had seen a "yellowish" animal "slightly bigger than a fox, more like a cat" crossing the bottom of his long garden in Shaftesbury.

Catwatching

The idea of going out to try to watch or photograph a British Big Cat is starting to appeal to an increasing number of people. The value of a good photograph, properly authenticated is difficult to assess. Certainly hundreds of pounds have been paid for out of focus pictures of large domestic cats and cuddly toys, and it seems likely that for the right picture a national newspaper would pay a good fee.

It should be borne in mind though that the chance of success is very limited. A good camera with a telephoto lens would be essential and a commitment of hundreds of hours spent in an active territory would be essential. Even then a picture could not be guaranteed. Using remote camera equipment does possibly reduce the personal time commitment, but there is the risk of relatively expensive equipment being stolen, and of getting thousands of pictures of more common British fauna, plus the odd courting couple!

Most wildlife biologists are fairly protective about these animals, some people who hunt are not. Accordingly anyone who does take a good picture of wild puma or lynx should consider carefully when selling the picture about the consequences of doing

Below: Caves cut into the Portland limestone at Winspit, near Worth Matravers. Jonathan McGowan suggests that caves like these may be occasional dens for big cats.

so. In particular the danger of giving away a very recent location of an animal might pinpoint its position for potential hunters.

A picture could of course be sold several days after it was taken, when the animal has moved out of the area. Alternatively the newspaper may be asked to remove from the picture any features that identify the locality. In these circumstances the photographer only reveals that the picture was taken within 3 miles of the village of X or Y.

Safety should also be considered when attempting to watch these animals. There have been a dozen or so allegations of attacks by British big cats. Only two of these victims actually show injuries that are consistent with such an attack. In both those cases the injuries were relatively minor, and did not, as far as I know, require overnight admission to hospital for treatment. There are a number of reports of large cats approaching people and only departing when shouted at, or having a stick waved at them.

The standard advice with such a close encounter is <u>not</u> to run, make yourself look as big as possible and make a lot of noise. Pumas in particular are often reported to be inquisitive and may observe someone from a distance for some time without necessarily considering attacking them. Although pumas and leopards are known to have killed people it is very rare and usually involves people putting themselves at risk in areas where the animals are known to be present.

On a practical level the dangers of any field work realistically come from domestic livestock and indigenous wildlife. People die every year in this country from contact with cows, bulls, bees and wasps. Falling off cliffs and out of trees (if climbing for a better view) also pose real dangers that can be avoided. Getting lost in adverse weather is also a very real risk. All these practical risks can be avoided or reduced by basic precautions such as checking the weather forecast, wearing the right clothes, taking a map, and leaving details of where you are going and a "back before time" with a responsible person. As the desk sergeant said in the morning briefing on Hill Street Blues, "Remember take care out there".

Conclusions

One of the problems with trying to make any sensible conclusions with such sporadic sightings of a diversity of cat-like animals is that we neither know the number of species or of individuals. From the regularity of certain descriptions it seems apparent that there is at least one large black cat, which most witnesses believe to be a black panther (leopard) regularly in the county, with possibly three such animals. If that is so it would appear that the territories are one in west Dorset (the Bridport/Beaminster area), one in central Dorset (Portland and north), and one in east Dorset that spends some of its time across the border in Hampshire and the New Forest. Animals may move between these territories of course, either seeking a mate, or seeking new territories. In view of the length of time that the sightings have occurred over, it is possible that these are in fact established territories which may have been occupied by successive individual cats.

There have also been a number of reports of lynx-type cats and of smaller feral-type tabby cats (but still bigger than the average domestic), particularly around the Portland area. As ambush hunters that like woodland, the lynx would be less likely to enter open ground than other species and would therefore only be seen occasionally. The lynx could have been an illegal re-introduction for either hunting, or an attempt to reduce the deer and rabbit populations. However the animal(s) came to be there, the number of alleged sightings of lynx in the Weymouth area in 2005 is highly suggestive of the genuine presence of such an animal.

The smaller cats could be one of the exotic species; a jungle cat was killed on a road in Hampshire in 1988 and another one was killed near Warminster in Wiltshire in 1995. These two animals effectively straddle the county of Dorset and do raise questions about whether there could be a small wild population in existence. (Another jungle cat was found dead by the roadside in Ludlow, Shropshire, in 1989 and there is a suggestion that he sired hybrid kittens to a local farm cat). Animals such as the jungle cat may, because of their size, be mistaken from a distance for domestic cats.

Alternatively feral (domestic) cats might be seen and mistaken for something larger. Although there is no scientific evidence of domestic cats becoming larger when they go feral there is much anecdotal evidence of this, and in New Zealand there is even film footage of feral domestic cats attacking lambs.

Whilst a number of sheep kills have been recorded, as have attacks on other domestic livestock, it should be considered that for the majority of the time the cats seem to feed on wildlife, particularly rabbits and deer. In view of the damage these animals do to crops and agricultural land generally, the presence of a few predators feeding regularly on them probably outweighs the loss of the odd sheep.

On a lighter note

There have been a number of hoax photographs of big cats in the United Kingdom based on slightly out of focus pictures of either cardboard cut out "cats" or large cuddly toys. The best known one was possibly the "Cuddly Toy of Cwmbran" which, in April 2005 caused some embarrassment to two national newspapers when they published the picture together with statements from various "experts" as to its authenticity.

A slightly different problem occurred with a cuddly toy a few months later in Shaftesbury. The details of this incident were revealed in the response to a Freedom of Information Act request on big cat sightings to Dorset Police.

The first telephone call was received by the police control room at 02:24 am when the caller explained that he had bought what he thought was a stuffed tiger for £29.99 in a local shop. He had just put a pen across its paws and they moved. He was now convinced that it was alive. A further call was received at 04:30 am when the caller was advised to go to bed and close the door after him. The third telephone call came in at 08:59 am when the caller was told that he should take the tiger back to the shop, as he had obviously brought the wrong item home!

Further Reading

There are no books which deal with the alien big cats of Dorset specifically. The following are books which either deal with the phenomenon generally or deal with it in neighbouring counties specifically. Although trying to cover the topic on a national basis Merrily Harpur's book does have several Dorset reports in it. This is perhaps not surprising as Merrily is based in the county for part of the year and is also responsible for the excellent website of the Dorset big cat register.

Fraser, M. (Ed.) (2006) *The Big Cats in Britain Yearbook 2006 CFZ*, Bideford

Harpur, M. (2006) *Mystery Big Cats,* Heart of Albion, Loughborough

Moiser, C. (2005) *Big Cat Mysteries of Somerset,* Bossiney Books, Launceston.

Newland, R.J., North, M.J. (2002) *Dark Dorset,* Oakmagic Publications Weston Super Mare.

Shuker, K (1989) *Mystery Cats of the World,* Robert Hale, London.

Yalden, D. (1999) *The History of British Mammals,* T & A.D. Poyser, London

Two national magazines, Animals and Men (from the North Devon Centre for Fortean Zoology), and Fortean Times both frequently carry reports of big cat sightings.

For up to date information it is also worth looking at the website of the various local newspapers. If they have an archive section this is also worth searching using terms such as "big cat" and "panther", possibly in conjunction with known locations of regular sightings.

The Big Cats in Britain Research Group are a national group who maintain a website (www.bigcatsinbritain.org) where they try to list, and record, every newspaper report that relates to big cats seen in the United Kingdom and Eire. They also carry a list of representatives, many of whom are willing to give talks, chat to witnesses, look at livestock kills and advise on livestock protection.

The Dark Dorset group also have a website which is a compendium of information relating to local folklore and mysteries. It is on www. darkdorset.co.uk

On a more local basis the Dorset Big Cats Register records a number of details of sightings and is available on www.dorsetbigcats.org.

The Centre for Fortean Zoology is an organisation studying Fortean, zoological and cryptozoological phenomena across the world. They have a magazine and website - www.cfz.org.uk

At the time of writing (January 2007) Jonathan McGowan of the Bournemouth Natural History Society is also continuing to research big cats in the Dorset area.